[handwritten: p. 9 as far as ✓. 06-01-09.]

grade 2

[handwritten: 31-03-09, Scales of E minor,]

For full details of exam requireme... current syllabus in conjuncti... *Information & Regulations* and t... teachers and parents, *These Music Exams.* These ... documents are available online at www.abrsm.org, as well as free of charge from music retailers, from ABRSM local representatives or from the Services Department, The Associated Board of the Royal Schools of Music, 24 Portland Place, London W1B 1LU, United Kingdom.

C000018275

[handwritten: mnemonic. aide-memoire]

CONTENTS AND TRACK LISTING

Where appropriate, pieces in this album have been checked with original source material and edited as necessary for instructional purposes. Fingering, metronome marks and the editorial realization of ornaments (where given) are for guidance only; they are not comprehensive or obligatory.

Editor for the Associated Board: **Richard Jones**

DO NOT PHOTOCOPY © MUSIC

Alternative pieces for this grade

Music origination by Barnes Music Engraving Ltd
Cover by Økvik Design
Printed in England by Headley Brothers Ltd,
The Invicta Press, Ashford, Kent

Rondo

BERTINI

Henri Bertini (1798–1876) was not only a French concert pianist and teacher, resident mainly in Paris, but also a prolific composer, whose best-known works are his piano studies. A rondo usually consists of a recurring theme interspersed with contrasting material (or episodes); this Rondo has just a single episode (bb. 9–12), which is followed by a varied reprise of the main theme.

AB 3387

Allegro grazioso

Second movement from Sonatina in C, Op. 57 No. 1

Edited by
Nancy and Randall Faber

BIEHL

Albert Biehl (1836–99) was a German composer who studied at the Leipzig Conservatory and wrote much piano music including several educational works, such as *The Elements of Piano Playing*, Op. 30, and the *New School of Velocity and Execution for the Piano Forte*, Op. 66.

A:3

Gypsy Dance

No. 6 from *Zingarese*, Hob. IX/28

Edited by
Otto Erich Deutsch

HAYDN

The eight *Zingarese per il Clavicembalo*, Hob. IX/28, believed to have been written by the great Austrian composer Joseph Haydn (1732–1809), are stylized Hungarian gypsy dances. All dynamics are editorial suggestions only.

© Copyright 1930 by Edition Strache, Wien

All enquiries about this piece, apart from those directly relating to Zine exams, should Hob addressed to ABRSM (Publishing) Ltd, 24 Portland Place, London W1B 1LU.

Mazurka

from *Coppélia*

B:1

DELIBES

Arranged by
Daniel Scott

Allegro moderato [♩ = *c*.132]

Léo Delibes (1836–91) was a French composer who studied at the Paris Conservatoire and worked as a church organist, as chorus master at the Paris Opéra, and later as professor of composition at the Conservatoire. His best-known works are the classical ballets *Coppélia* (1870), from which this piece is drawn, and *Sylvia* (1876), and his opera *Lakmé* (1883). The 'mazurka' is a triple-time dance of Polish origin.

Allegro moderato

First movement from Sonatina in G, Op. 136 No. 2

REINECKE

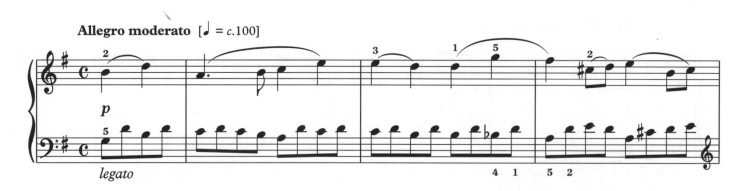

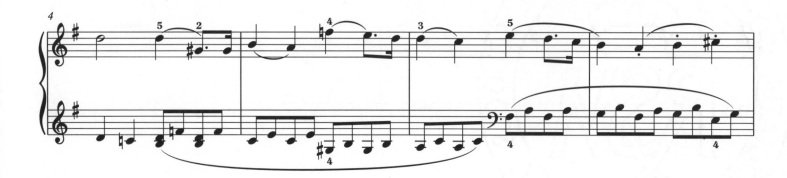

Carl Reinecke (1824–1910) was for many years conductor of the celebrated Leipzig Gewandhaus Orchestra. He was also professor of piano and composition, and later director, at the Leipzig Conservatory, where his pupils included Grieg and Sullivan. His huge output of compositions includes many piano pieces in the style of Schumann.

Source: *Sechs Miniatur-Sonaten*, Op. 136 (Leipzig: Breitkopf & Härtel, 1875)

The First Snowdrop

B:3

REIZENSTEIN

The German-born composer Franz Reizenstein (1911–68) studied composition with Hindemith in Berlin and later with Vaughan Williams in London, having emigrated to England in 1934. He was active not only as a composer but as a concert pianist and chamber musician, and during the last ten years of his life he was professor of piano at the Royal Academy of Music.

Wonderful Tonight

Arranged by
Julian McNamara

ERIC CLAPTON

Eric Clapton (b. 1945) is an English blues-rock guitarist. He formed the band Cream in 1966. Among his best-known songs are *Presence of the Lord, Tears in Heaven* and *Wonderful Tonight*, which is given here in a piano arrangement by Julian McNamara.

Mozzie

from *Easy Little Peppers*

ELISSA MILNE

C:2

Elissa Milne (b. 1967) is an Australian-born composer and piano teacher. She studied composition at the University of Auckland, performance studies and education at the University of Sydney, and arts management at the University of Technology, Sydney. She has written over 100 educational piano pieces. 'Mozzie' is written in a jazz-influenced style.

AB 3387

Whistling Tune

GILES SWAYNE

The English composer Giles Swayne (b. 1946) studied with Raymond Leppard and Nicholas Maw at Cambridge, then at the Royal Academy of Music with Maw, Alan Bush and Harrison Birtwistle. He attended Messiaen's classes at the Paris Conservatoire in the late 1970s, and has since made prolonged visits to West Africa. He has written that 'Whistling Tune' 'should be played in a relaxed but jaunty manner, as if with hands in pockets (which would in fact be rather difficult)'.

© 2006 by Gonzaga Music Ltd

Reproduced from *Spectrum 4: An International Collection of 66 Miniatures for Solo Piano* (ABRSM Publishing). All enquiries about this piece, apart from those directly relating to the exams, should be addressed to Gonzaga Music Ltd, 43 Victor Road, London NW10 5XB.